Supporting
Phonics
and
Spelling

FOR AGES 10–11

Andrew Brodie

Contents

Andrew Brodie: Supporting Phonics & Spelling © A & C Black Publishers Ltd. 2006

Introduction

Supporting Phonics and Spelling is aimed at children in mainstream classrooms who have been identified as needing 'additional' or 'different' literacy support, particularly in phonics and spelling. The activities can be used by anyone working with children who fall into this category, whether you are a teacher, classroom assistant or parent.

Typically the ten to eleven year-old children for whom the book is intended will be working at the levels expected of Year 4 or Year 5 or may simply need extra help in tackling the level of work appropriate for Year 6. Their difficulties may be short-term, and could be overcome with extra practice and support on a one-to-one or small group basis, or they may be long-term, where such support enables them to make progress but at a level behind their peer group. The activities in this book provide exactly what these children need – systematic repetition and practice of early phonic skills, based on a strong foundation of synthetic phonics and the best features of analytic phonics. The *Supporting Phonics and Spelling* series reflects the best practice in teaching spelling through phonics. It provides an approach that is:

- Systematic
- Multi-sensory
- Based on speaking and listening
- Linked closely to reading skills

This book is organised into three-page sets. It is vital that the teaching assistant or class teacher reads the 'Teacher's notes' on 'Sheet a' before starting the lesson. This first page in each set introduces specific phonemes and provides a good opportunity for the teacher and child to sound them out together. Children can also use their multi-sensory skills at this stage by drawing the letters in sand or making them out of dough or modelling clay. The second worksheet revises the same phonemes, but with a particular emphasis on speaking, listening and writing. The final worksheet in the set features a list of words containing the phonemes for further practice and consolidation. When used together, the three worksheets provide a thorough grounding in the phonic knowledge and skills that children need for confident reading, writing and spelling.

All the worksheets can be used on their own or alongside other literacy schemes that are already established within your school. The activities are simple and self-explanatory and the instruction text is deliberately kept to a minimum to make the pages easy to use for adults and less daunting for children to follow.

We recommend that the children use the *Supporting Phonics and Spelling* worksheets on a daily basis for approximately 20 minutes. Regular practice of previous learning is an integral part of the series. In completing the activities, teachers should place particular emphasis on speaking and listening skills. Most of the three-page sets include the opportunity to use dictation, a teaching method that may be considered old-fashioned, but when used appropriately can be both fun and rewarding. Opportunities will arise to dictate sounds, whole words and whole sentences. Initially, pupils might need help with each of these but will soon gain confidence as they experience increasing and visible success.

Children generally achieve the greatest success in an atmosphere of support and encouragement. Praise from a caring adult can be the best reward for the children's efforts. The worksheets and activities in this book will provide many opportunities for children to enjoy these successes. The development of a positive attitude and the resulting increase in self-esteem will help them with all of their schoolwork.

Definitions and explanations of terms

(Please note that some publications will give slightly different definitions.)

Phoneme
A phoneme is a unit of sound and can be represented by:
one letter e.g. /b/ as in **b**at   two letters e.g. /ee/ as in sw**ee**t
three letters e.g. /ear/ as in n**ear**
Note that a phoneme can be represented in several different ways
e.g. the sound /ee/ can be represented by:

ee as in f**ee**t	**ei** as in c**ei**ling	**ie** as in ch**ie**f
ea as in n**ea**t	**i** as in sk**i**	**e_e** as in P**e**t**e**

Vowel phoneme
A vowel phoneme makes an open sound and always contains at least one vowel – you usually have to open your mouth to say it.
Examples of vowel phonemes are:

/a/ as in b**a**t	/ie/ as in cr**ie**s	/oo/ as in b**oo**k
/ur/ as in t**ur**n	/ow/ as in t**ow**n	

Consonant phoneme
A consonant phoneme always contains at least one consonant and usually involves closing the mouth, 'biting' the lower lip, or touching the roof of the mouth with the tongue. (There are exceptions e.g. /h/). Examples of consonant phonemes are:

/b/ as in **b**at	/f/ as in **ph**otograph
/th/ as in **th**ey	/ng/ as in si**ng**

Grapheme
A grapheme is a letter, a pair of letters or a group of letters representing a single sound e.g. **ee**, **ei**, **ie**, **ea**, **i** and **e_e** are all graphemes representing the sound /ee/.

Grapheme/phoneme correspondence
The relationship between letters and the sounds that they represent.

Digraph
A digraph consists of two letters representing a single sound. So, for example, the grapheme **ch** is a consonant digraph because it is made up of two consonants. The grapheme **ee** is a vowel digraph and although it contains a consonant, **ow** is also a vowel digraph, because it makes an open sound like a vowel does.

Split digraph
A split digraph consists of two vowels separated by a consonant to make one phoneme e.g.   **e_e** as in P**e**t**e**   **i_e** as in m**i**n**e**   **a_e** as in c**a**m**e**

Trigraph
A trigraph is a group of three letters representing a single sound.
The vowel phonemes /air/ and /ear/ are trigraphs.

Cluster
A cluster consists of two or more letters making more than one sound. For example:
t   h   r   are three letters that can make the cluster **thr**, which consists of the phonemes /th/ and /r/.

Blending
Blending is the process of combining different sounds (phonemes) to be able to say a particular word or to make up part of a word e.g.
/sh/   /i/   /p/   can be blended to make the word ship.

/th/   /r/   are blended to make the cluster **thr**. Sometimes a cluster like this will be called a blend.

Segmenting
Segmenting is the process of splitting a word into its different phonemes to be able to spell it e.g. **ship** can be segmented into the three phonemes /sh/ /i/ /p/.

Onset and rime
The terms 'onset' and 'rime' are used together when analysing words. For example, in the word 'cat' the phoneme represented by the letter 'c' is described as the onset and the final cluster 'at' is described as the rime. Note that words that end with a particular rime always rhyme but words that rhyme do not always contain the same rime! For example, cat, rat and bat all end with the rime 'at' and all rhyme. But the words tough and muff rhyme but have the rimes 'ough' and 'uff'.

vc
vowel/consonant e.g. the word *it*

cv
consonant/vowel e.g. the word *be*

cvc
consonant/vowel/consonant e.g. the word *cat*

ccvc
consonant/consonant/vowel/consonant e.g. the word *shop*

cvcc
consonant/vowel/consonant/consonant e.g. the word *fast*

Andrew Brodie: Supporting Phonics & Spelling © A & C Black Publishers Ltd. 2006

An introduction to phonemes

Language can be analysed by considering the separate sounds that combine to make up spoken words. These sounds are called phonemes and the English language has more than forty of them. It is possible to concentrate on forty-two main phonemes but here we list forty-four phonemes including those that are commonly used only in some regions of the country.

It is helpful to look at each phoneme individually and then at some sample words that demonstrate how the phoneme is represented by different graphemes as shown in the list below. Try reading each word out loud to spot the phoneme in each one. For the simple vowel sounds the graphemes are shown in bold text.

Vowel phonemes	Sample words
/a/	b**a**t
/e/	l**e**g, g**ue**ss, h**ea**d, s**ai**d, s**ay**s
/i/	b**i**g, plant**e**d, b**u**sy, cr**y**stal, d**e**cide, **e**xact, g**ui**lt, r**e**peat
/o/	d**o**g, **ho**nest, w**a**s, qu**a**rrel, tr**ou**gh, v**au**lt, y**ach**t (the ch is silent)
/u/	b**u**g, l**o**ve, bl**oo**d, c**o**mfort, r**ou**gh, y**ou**ng
/ae/	rain, day, game, navy, weigh, they, great, rein
/ee/	been, team, field, these, he, key, litre, quay, suite
/ie/	pie, high, sign, my, bite, child, guide, guy, haiku
/oe/	boat, goes, crow, cone, gold, sew
/ue/	soon, do, July, blue, chew, June, bruise, shoe, you, move, through
/oo/	book, put
/ar/	barn, bath (regional), laugh (regional), baa, half, clerk, heart, guard
/ur/	Thursday, girl, her, learn, word
/or/	born, door, warm, all, draw, cause, talk, aboard, abroad, before, four, bought, taught
/ow/	brown, found, plough
/oi/	join, toy, buoy
/air/	chair, pear, care, where, their, prayer
/ear/	near, cheer, here, weird, pier

Try saying this vowel phoneme in the sample words:

/er/ fast**er**, g**a**zump, curr**a**nt, wooll**e**n, circ**u**s

Not to be confused with the phoneme /ur/, this phoneme is very similar to /u/ but is slightly different in some regions.

Consonant phonemes with sample words

/b/	bag, rub
/d/	dad, could
/f/	off, calf, fast, graph, tough
/g/	ghost, girl, bag
/h/	here, who
/j/	bridge, giraffe, huge, jet
/k/	kite, antique, cat, look, quiet, choir, sock, six (note that the sound made by the letter x is a blend of the phonemes /k/ and /s/)
/l/	leg, crawl, full
/m/	mug, climb, autumn
/n/	now, gnash, knight, sign, fun
/p/	peg, tap
/r/	run, wrote
/s/	cinema, goose, listen, psalm, scene, see, sword, yes, less
/t/	ten, sit, receipt
/v/	vest, love
/w/	wet
/wh/	when (regional)
/y/	yes
/z/	choose, was, zoo
/th/	the, with
/th/	thank, path
/ch/	cheer, such, match
/sh/	shop, rush, session, chute
/zh/	usual
/ng/	thing, think

For some phonemes you may dispute some of the examples that we have listed. This may be due to regional variations in pronunciation. Disputing the sounds is a positive step as it ensures that you are analysing them!

It is not necessary to teach the children all the graphemes for each phoneme but to be ready and aware when pupils suggest words to you to represent a particular sound. They are not wrong with their suggestions and should be praised for recognising the phoneme. You can then show them how the words that they have suggested are written but that normally the particular sound is represented by a specific grapheme.

Andrew Brodie: Supporting Phonics & Spelling © A & C Black Publishers Ltd. 2006

Examining the list of medium frequency words

These words from the medium frequency list for Years 4 and 5 do not always follow simple phonic patterns, although all of them include phonic elements that follow a typical pattern. Children will find them easier to tackle through developing the phonic skills that we are encouraging in this series of books: listening to sounds, speaking the sounds clearly and segmenting words into sounds that can be matched to appropriate letters, i.e. matching phonemes to appropriate graphemes.

above	can't	half	often	sure	white
across	change	happy	only	swimming	whole
almost	children	head	opened	think	why
along	clothes	heard	other	those	window
also	coming	high	outside	thought	without
always	didn't	I'm	own	through	woke
animals	different	important	paper	today	woken
any	does	inside	place	together	word
around	don't	jumped	right	told	work
asked	during	knew	round	tries	world
baby	earth	know	second	turned	write
balloon	every	lady	show	under	year
before	eyes	leave	sister	until	young
began	father	light	small	upon	
being	first	might	something	used	
below	following	money	sometimes	walked	
better	found	morning	sound	walking	
between	friends	mother	started	watch	
birthday	garden	much	still	where	
both	goes	near	stopped	while	
brother	gone	never	such		
brought	great	number	suddenly		

Some of these words are included in the phonic lists in this book and some are included as 'odd ones out'. You may like to introduce other words from the list as opportunities arise, supporting the children in segmenting the words to be able to spell them. Below is the list of focus words that appear in this book, though many others are included within the activities.

ache	chemistry	filthiness	knock	quarter	there
act	children	filthy	knot	quiet	though
actual	choir	flavour	know	quite	thought
actually	Christmas	friends	lamb	quiz	through
air	clasp	gasp	laugh	raspberry	thumb
answer	climb	glisten	laughed	repair	together
antique	clothes	gnaw	limb	respect	tough
asked	colour	guilty	listen	salt	uncomfortable
autumn	comb	hair	lunch	scare	wasp
bear	comfortable	half	melt	school	wealth
behaviour	coming	halves	middle	share	wealthy
belt	cough	headache	mistletoe	sign	wear
bench	crumb	health	money	soften	wearing
between	dare	healthiness	morning	something	where
beware	daughter	healthy	munch	spare	whisper
bolt	design	horrible	naughtier	sprinkle	whistle
bomb	different	hospital	naughtiness	square	who
bought	doctor	hour	naughty	squash	winch
branch	echo	hymn	neighbour	stairs	wisp
brought	effect	important	octagon	stare	without
built	enough	inch	October	stomach	wrap
bunch	fact	journey	orchestra	suddenly	wriggle
calf	fair	kettle	ought	swear	write
calves	fairy	kilt	pair	swimming	writing
care	fasten	knee	pear	sword	wrong
castle	favour	kneel	pinch	table	wrote
caught	favourite	knife	plumber	taught	
chair	felt	knight	quality	tear	
change	filth	knives	quantity	terrible	

	Learning objective	
1a	**Phonemes** **Consonants:** /w/,/s/,/p/,/c/,/l/,/g/,/r/,/b/, /h/,/t/,/m/,/n/,/ng/ **Vowels:** /o/ (as in wasp), /i/,/or/,/e/, /ar/ or /a/ (regional)	**Target words** wasp, clasp, gasp, raspberry, whisper, wisp, respect, hospital, morning

Worksheet 1a

- Photocopy this page and ask the child to cut out the target words.

- Discuss the words and what each word means. Help the child to read them by blending the phonemes.

- Ask him/her to identify the sounds in some of the words, the /w/, /o/, /s/ and /p/ in the word *wasp*, for example.

- It would be helpful to discuss syllables, reminding children of the number of syllables in the name of the school or the name of your town or village, before looking at the consonant cluster **sp**. In the single syllable words the phonemes /s/ and /p/ blend together. In words with more than one syllable they tend to form separate sounds at the end and beginning of syllables. Discuss this with the child, encouraging him/her to sound out words such as *respect*. Notice also that many people do not sound the letter **p** in the word *raspberry*.

- Discuss which word is the 'odd one out' from the list – *morning* because it does not contain the blend **sp**.

Worksheet 1b

- Discuss the words at the top of the sheet before dictating the following sentences to the child:

  One morning I was just about to pick a raspberry when a wasp stung me.
  The clasp on the suitcase has broken.
  The audience gave a loud gasp when the magician appeared to cut the lady in half.

- S/he may need some help in segmenting each word into its phonemes to make it easier to spell. Say each word repeatedly and slowly, encouraging the child to hear the separate sounds.

- As an extra activity ask the child to make up a sentence and to write it down. Encourage him/her to write clearly, following the school's handwriting policy for letter formation, and to start each sentence with a capital letter and to end it with a full stop.

Worksheet 1c

- This sheet includes the nine target words.

- It can be copied so that the left hand side can be used for display purposes and the right hand side can be used to provide the child with extra practice in writing the words. You could write each word on the first of the two writing lines so that the child can copy your writing underneath in the correct style used by your school.

TARGET WORDS

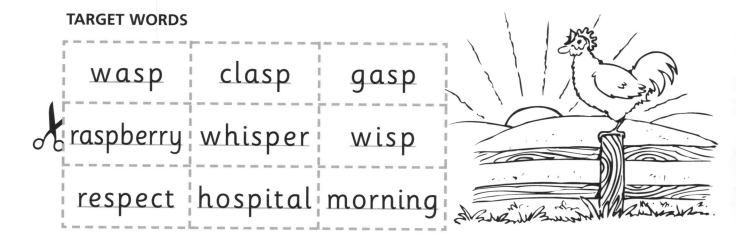

wasp	clasp	gasp
raspberry	whisper	wisp
respect	hospital	morning

Name: **Date:**

Read these words because you will need them in your sentences.

just about pick stung suitcase broken
audience loud magician appeared lady half

Listen to your teacher. Write the sentences.

one
Won morning I was just abot to picke
rasdary when e wasp stung my
berry   me.

The clase on the suitcase has droken

Now write your own sentence.

Name: _____ **Date:** _____

Words for today

wasp _____

clasp _____

gasp _____

raspberry _____

whisper _____

wisp _____

respect _____

hospital _____

morning _____

Andrew Brodie: Supporting Phonics & Spelling © A & C Black Publishers Ltd. 2006

Learning objective

Phonemes
Consonants: /f/,/c/,/t/,/l/,/g/,/n/,/b/,/d/, /s/,/m/,/th/,/ng/
Vowels: /a/,/ue/,/u/,/i/,/e/,/o/,/oe/,/er/

Target words
act, fact, actual, actually, effect, octagon, October, doctor, something

Worksheet 2a

- Photocopy this page and ask the child to cut out the target words.
- Discuss the words and what each word means. Help the child to read them by blending the phonemes.
- Ask him/her to identify the sounds in some of the words, the /f/, /a/, /k/ and /t/ in the word *fact*, for example. Discuss which word is the 'odd one out' from the list.

Worksheet 2b

- Dictate the words **act, fact, actual, actually, effect, octagon, October, doctor, something** to create the word bank at the top of the sheet. The child may need some help in segmenting each word into its phonemes to make it easier to spell. Say each word repeatedly and slowly, encouraging him/her to hear the separate sounds.
- Ensure that the child has spelt all the words correctly, and that s/he has written the month *October* with a capital **O**, before asking him/her to fill in the gaps in the sentences.
- As an extra activity ask the child to make up a sentence using some of the target words and to write it down. Encourage the child to write clearly, following the school's handwriting policy for letter formation, and to start each sentence with a capital letter and to end it with a full stop.

Worksheet 2c

- This sheet includes the nine target words.
- It can be copied so that the left hand side can be used for display purposes and the right hand side can be used to provide the child with extra practice in writing the words. You could write each word on the first of the two writing lines so that the child can copy your writing underneath in the correct style used by your school.

TARGET WORDS

act	fact	actual
actually	effect	octagon
October	doctor	something

2b

Listen to your teacher. Write the words in the word bank.

WORD BANK

⭐ Use the correct words to fill in the gaps in the sentences.

In _____ I am going to
_____ in a play.

The teacher gave me _____
to do in wet playtime.

I went to see the _____
at the hospital.

⭐ Write your own sentence using words from the word bank.

Andrew Brodie: Supporting Phonics & Spelling © A & C Black Publishers Ltd. 2006

Name: _____ **Date:** _____

Words for today

act _____

fact _____

actual _____

actually _____

effect _____

octagon _____

October _____

doctor _____

something _____

Learning objective

Phonemes
Consonants: /s/,/b/,/l/,/t/,/f/,/m/,/n/,/k/,/g/,/d/
Vowels: /e/,/o/ (as grapheme a), /i/ (as grapheme ui),
/oe/,/er/,/u/

Target words
salt, belt, felt, melt,
built, guilty, kilt, bolt,
different

Worksheet 3a

- Photocopy this page and ask the child to cut out the target words.
- Discuss the words and what each word means. Help the child to read them by blending the phonemes.
- Ask him/her to identify the sounds in some of the words. Encourage the child to say each word carefully. Can s/he hear that the letter **a** in *salt* makes the /o/ sound? Point out the spelling of the phoneme /i/ in the words *built* and *guilty* and compare these words to *kilt*.
- Discuss which word is the 'odd one out' from the list.

Worksheet 3b

- Help the child to write the words in alphabetical order. S/he may need help in segmenting each word into its phonemes to make it easier to spell. Say each word repeatedly and slowly, encouraging the child to hear the separate sounds.
- Ask him/her to create oral sentences which include some of the words or related words, then to write down one of the sentences e.g. *The boy felt guilty when he broke the window. The old school was built over a hundred years ago. She wore a different belt in her jeans.* Encourage the child to write clearly, following the school's handwriting policy for letter formation, and to start each sentence with a capital letter and to end it with a full stop.

Worksheet 3c

- This sheet includes the nine target words.
- It can be copied so that the left hand side can be used for display purposes and the right hand side can be used to provide the child with extra practice in writing the words. You could write each word on the first of the two writing lines so that the child can copy your writing in the correct style used by your school.

TARGET WORDS

salt	belt	felt
melt	built	guilty
kilt	bolt	different

Name: _____   **Date:** _____

Read the words in the word bank.

 **WORD BANK**

salt	belt	felt	melt	built	guilty

kilt   bolt   different

Write the words in alphabetical order.

_____   _____   _____

_____   _____   _____

_____   _____   _____

Now write these **lt** words.

alter	halt	fault

malt	hilt	lilt

wilt	colt	jolt

Write a sentence containing at least one **lt** word.

_____

_____

_____

Name: _____   **Date:** _____

Words for today

salt   _____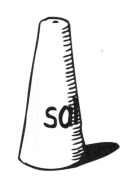

belt   _____

felt   _____

melt   _____

built   _____

guilty   _____

kilt   _____

bolt   _____

different   _____

Andrew Brodie: Supporting Phonics & Spelling © A & C Black Publishers Ltd. 2006

4a

Learning objective

Phonemes
Consonants: /b/,/r/,/ch/,/p/,/w/,/l/,/m/, /f/,/n/,/d/,/z/
Vowels: /a/ or /ar/ (regional), /i/,/e/,/u/

Target words
branch, inch, pinch, winch, bench, bunch, lunch, munch, friends

Worksheet 4a
- Photocopy this page and ask the child to cut out the target words.
- Discuss the words and what each word means. Help the child to read them by blending the phonemes.
- Ask him/her to identify the sounds in some of the words, the /b/, /r/, /a/, /n/ and /ch/ in the word *branch*, for example.
- Discuss which word is the 'odd one out' from the list – *friends* because it does not contain the blend **nch**.

Worksheet 4b
- Discuss the words at the top of the sheet before dictating the following sentences to the child:

  Some people used a truck with a winch to drag away the fallen branch.
  I like to munch my lunch with my friends.
  I pinched myself when I squashed my leg between two chairs.

- S/he may need help in segmenting each word into its phonemes to make it easier to spell. Say each word repeatedly and slowly, encouraging the child to hear the separate sounds.
- As an extra activity ask the child to make up a sentence and to write it down. Encourage him/her to write clearly, following the school's handwriting policy for letter formation, and to start each sentence with a capital letter and to end it with a full stop.

Worksheet 4c
- This sheet includes the nine target words.
- It can be copied so that the left hand side can be used for display purposes and the right hand side can be used to provide the child with extra practice in writing the words. You could write each word on the first of the two writing lines so that the child can copy your writing in the correct style used by your school.

TARGET WORDS

branch	inch	pinch
winch	bench	bunch
lunch	munch	friends

Name: **Date:**

Read these words because you will need them in your sentences.

some	people	used	truck	fallen
myself	when	squashed	between	

⭐ Listen to your teacher. Write the sentences.

_____

_____

_____

_____

                    _____

                    _____

                    _____

_____

_____

_____

⭐ Now write a sentence of your own.

_____

_____

_____

Words for today

branch _____

inch _____

pinch _____

winch _____

bench _____

bunch _____

lunch _____

munch _____

friends _____

Learning objective

5a

Phonemes
Consonants: /w/,/l/,/th/,/h/,/s/,/n/,/f/
Vowels: /e/ (as grapheme ea), /ee/ (y and i), /e/,/i/

Target words
wealth, healthy, wealthy, health, filth, healthiness, filthy, money, filthiness

Worksheet 5a

- Photocopy this page and ask the child to cut out the target words.
- Discuss the words and what each word means. Help the child to read them by blending the phonemes.
- Ask him/her to identify the sounds in some of the words, the /w/, /e/, /l/ and /th/ in the word *wealth*, for example. Discuss the fact that *money* is the 'odd one out' from the list as it does not contain the cluster **lth**.
- Help the child to notice that the letter **y** can be added to *wealth* or to *health* to make related words, but that when the word is further extended the **y** is removed and replaced by letter **i**.

Worksheet 5b

- Dictate the words **wealth, healthy, wealthy, health, filth, healthiness, filthy, money, filthiness** in random order to create the word bank at the top of the sheet. S/he may need help in segmenting each word into its phonemes to make it easier to spell. Say each word repeatedly and slowly, encouraging the child to hear the separate sounds.
- Ensure that the child has spelt all the words correctly, before asking him/her to fill in the gaps in the sentences.
- As an extra activity ask the child to make up a sentence using some of the target words and to write it down. Encourage him/her to write clearly, following the school's handwriting policy for letter formation, and to start each sentence with a capital letter and to end it with a full stop.

Worksheet 5c

- This sheet includes the nine target words.
- It can be copied so that the left hand side can be used for display purposes and the right hand side can be used to provide the child with extra practice in writing the words. You could write each word on the first of the two writing lines so that the child can copy your writing in the correct style used by your school.

TARGET WORDS

wealth	healthy	wealthy
health	filth	healthiness
filthy	money	filthiness

Name: _____   **Date:** _____

Listen to your teacher. Write the words in the word bank.

WORD BANK

_____   _____   _____

_____   _____   _____

_____   _____   _____

Use the correct words to fill in the gaps in the sentences.

People who have lots of _____
are very _____ but it is more
important to be _____.

"Have you been rolling in the mud?" asked
Mum. "Your clothes are _____."
"No," replied Tariq. "The _____ is because
I was playing football at break time."

Now write a sentence of your own using the words from the word bank.

_____

_____

_____

Words for today

wealth _____

wealthy _____

health _____

healthy _____

healthiness _____

filth _____

filthy _____

filthiness _____

money _____

Learning objective

Phonemes **Consonants:** /f/,/h/,/p/,/s/,/t/,/ch/,/r/,/k/ (as grapheme c), /l/,/th/,/z/ **Vowels:** /air/,/ee/ (as grapheme y), /u/ (as grapheme e), /oe/	**Target words** air, fair, hair, pair, stairs, fairy, chair, repair, clothes

Worksheet 6a

- Photocopy this page and ask the child to cut out the target words.
- Discuss the words and what each word means. Help the child to read them by blending the phonemes.
- Ask him/her to identify the sounds in some of the words. Encourage the child to say each word carefully Can s/he hear that the letter **o** in the word *clothes* 'says its name' because of the letter **e** after the /th/? Discuss the fact that *clothes* is the 'odd one out' from the list because it does not contain the vowel phoneme /air/.

Worksheet 6b

- Help the child write the words in alphabetical order.
- S/he may need help in segmenting each word into its phonemes to make it easier to spell. Say each word repeatedly and slowly, encouraging the child to hear the separate sounds.
- Ask him/her to create oral sentences which include some of the words or related words and then to write down one of the sentences e.g. *The fairy with fair hair flew upstairs. "Don't tear your clothes because I don't want to repair them," said Dad.*
- Encourage the child to write clearly, following the school's handwriting policy for letter formation, and to start each sentence with a capital letter and to end it with a full stop.

Worksheet 6c

- This sheet includes the nine target words.
- It can be copied so that the left hand side can be used for display purposes and the right hand side can be used to provide the child with extra practice in writing the words. You could write each word on the first of the two writing lines so that the child can copy your writing underneath in the correct style used by your school.

TARGET WORDS

air	fair	hair
pair	stairs	fairy
chair	repair	clothes

Name: _____ **Date:** _____

Read the words in the word bank.

WORD BANK

| pair | chair | clothes | air | fairy | fair |

repair   hair   stairs

★ Write the words in alphabetical order.

_____   _____

_____   _____

_____   _____

_____

★ Now write these **air** words:

upstairs   downstairs

_____   _____

hairy   dairy

_____   _____

★ Write a sentence containing at least one **air** word.

_____

_____

Andrew Brodie: Supporting Phonics & Spelling © A & C Black Publishers Ltd. 2006

Name: _____ **Date:** _____

Words for today

air _____

fair _____

hair _____

pair _____

stairs _____

fairy _____

chair _____

repair _____

clothes _____

Learning objective

7a

Phonemes
Consonants: /s/,/k/(as graphemes c and q), /d/,/sh/,/t/,/p/,/w/,/b/,/n/,/l/
Vowels: /air/,/ee/,/u/

Target words
scare, care, dare, share, stare, spare, square, beware, suddenly

Worksheet 7a

- Photocopy this page and ask the child to cut out the target words.

- Discuss the words and what each word means. Help the child to read them by blending the phonemes.

- Ask him/her to identify the sounds in some of the words, the /s/, /k/ and /air/ in the word *scare*, for example. You may like to remind the pupils of the words in Set 6 as they also contained the phoneme /air/ but spelt differently.

- Discuss which word is the 'odd one out' from the list – *suddenly* because it does not contain the phoneme /air/.

Worksheet 7b

- Discuss the words at the top of the sheet before dictating the following short story to the pupil.

  "Do you dare go to the house where the big dog lives?" Asked my friends.
  "I don't care," I said. "I am not scared."
  I went to the house. There was a sign that said, 'Beware of the dog'.
  Suddenly I heard a very loud bark. I was scared and I ran away, but I didn't tell my friends.

- S/he may need help in segmenting each word into its phonemes to make it easier to spell. Speak slowly, encouraging the child to hear the separate sounds in each word.

- The child will need each sentence repeated several times and may need support with the punctuation. Take the opportunity to show him/her how the question mark, the comma and the full stop all go before the closing speech marks.

- As an extra activity ask the pupil to make up a sentence using the target words and to write it down. Encourage the child to write clearly, following the school's handwriting policy for letter formation, and to start each sentence with a capital letter and to end it with a full stop.

Worksheet 7c

- This sheet includes the nine target words.

- It can be copied so that the left hand side can be used for display purposes and the right hand side can be used to provide the child with extra practice in writing the words. You could write each word on the first of the two writing lines so that the child can copy your writing in the correct style used by your school.

TARGET WORDS

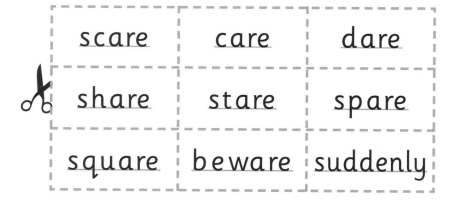

scare	care	dare
share	stare	spare
square	beware	suddenly

 26

Name: **Date:**

Read these words because you will need them in your story.

friends   asked   house   where
lives   don't   said   sign

Listen to your teacher. Write the story.

_____

_____

_____

_____

_____

_____

_____

_____

_____

_____

Now write a sentence of your own.

_____

_____

Words for today

scare   _____

care   _____

dare   _____

share   _____

stare   _____

spare   _____

square   _____

beware   _____

suddenly   _____

Learning objective

Phonemes
Consonants: /w/,/wh/,/p/,/b/,/t/,/s/,/th/,/ng/,/j/
Vowels: /air/ (as graphemes ear and ere), /i/,/ai/

Target words
wear, where, pear, bear, tear, swear, there, wearing, change

Worksheet 8a

- Photocopy this page and ask the child to cut out the target words.
- Discuss the words and what each word means. Help the child to read them by blending the phonemes.
- Ask him/her to identify the sounds in some of the words, the /w/ and /air/ in the word *wear* and the /wh/ and /air/ in the word *where*, for example. In most parts of the country these two words will sound the same (homophones) but in some regions the /h/ can be heard in the /wh/. Teach the child this clue: *Here and there are where the bear likes to wear his earphones.* Encourage him/her to notice that the word *where* is related to place and contains the word *here* whereas the word *wear* contains the word *ear*. Although phonetically this appears very confusing some children remember these clues very well.
- Discuss the fact that *change* is the 'odd one out' from the list as it does not contain the phoneme /air/.

Worksheet 8b

- Dictate the words **wear, where, pear, bear, tear, swear, there, wearing, change** in random order to create the word bank at the top of the sheet. The child may need help in segmenting each word into its phonemes to make it easier to spell. Say each word repeatedly and slowly, encouraging the child to hear the separate sounds. Ensure that the child has spelt all the words correctly, before asking him/her to fill in the gaps in the sentences.
- As an extra activity ask the child to make up a sentence including some of the target words and to write it down. Encourage the child to write clearly, following the school's handwriting policy for letter formation, and to start each sentence with a capital letter and to end it with a full stop.

Worksheet 8c

- This sheet includes the nine target words.
- It can be copied so that the left hand side can be used for display purposes and the right hand side can be used to provide the child with extra practice in writing the words. You could write each word on the first of the two writing lines so that the child can copy your writing underneath in the correct style used by your school.

TARGET WORDS

wear	where	pear
bear	tear	swear
there	wearing	change

Name: _____ **Date:** _____

Listen to your teacher. Write the words in the word bank.

WORD BANK

_____   _____   _____

_____   _____   _____

_____   _____   _____

★ Use the correct words to fill in the gaps in the sentences.

Here and _____ are _____ the
_____ likes to _____ his earphones.

It is very rude to _____.

I prefer _____ to apples.

"Why are you _____ your pyjamas?"
asked Mum. "You can't go to school in those.
Go and _____ into your uniform."

★ Now write a sentence of your own using the words from the word bank.

_____

_____

Andrew Brodie: Supporting Phonics & Spelling © A & C Black Publishers Ltd. 2006

8c

Name: _____   **Date:** _____

Words for today

wear   _____

where   _____

pear   _____

bear   _____

tear   _____

swear   _____

there   _____

wearing _____

change   _____

9a

Learning objective

Phonemes
Consonants: /f/,/h/,/p/,/s/,/t/,/ch/,/r/,
/k/ (as grapheme c), /l/,/th/,/z/
Vowels: /air/,/ee/ (as grapheme y),
/i/ (as grapheme e), /oe/

Target words
though, through, bought,
brought, thought, cough,
tough, enough, ought

Worksheet 9a

- Photocopy this page and ask the child to cut out the target words.
- Discuss the words and what each word means. Help the child to read them by blending the phonemes.
- Notice that we have not included an 'odd one out' in the list of words as the sounds represented by **ough** are incredibly complicated.
- Ask the child to identify the sounds in some of the words. Encourage him/her to say each word carefully. Can s/he hear that **ough** says /oe/ in *though*, /ue/ in *through*, and /or/ in *bought*? Can s/he hear that **ough** says /o/ /f/ in *cough* and /u/ /f/ in *tough*? Does s/he understand the distinction between words such as *bought* and *brought* or *though, thought* and *through*? Segmenting these words into their phonemes can help with both the spelling of the words and the understanding of their distinct meanings.

Worksheet 9b

- Help the child to write the words in alphabetical order. This will help him/her to distinguish between words that are very close in spelling – *though, through* and *thought*, for example. S/he may need help in segmenting each word into its phonemes to make it easier to spell. Say each word repeatedly and slowly, encouraging the child to hear the separate sounds.
- Ask him/her to create oral sentences to include some of the words or related words and then to write down one of the sentences e.g. *I bought a new pencil case and I brought it to school. I thought that the teacher came in through the window, though I didn't see it happen.*
- Encourage the child to write clearly, following the school's handwriting policy for letter formation, and to start each sentence with a capital letter and to end it with a full stop.

Worksheet 9c

- This sheet includes the nine target words.
- It can be copied so that the left hand side can be used for display purposes and the right hand side can be used to provide the child with extra practice in writing the words. You could write each word on the first of the two writing lines so that the child can copy your writing in the correct style used by your school.

TARGET WORDS

though	through	bought
brought	thought	cough
tough	enough	ought

Andrew Brodie: Supporting Phonics & Spelling © A & C Black Publishers Ltd. 2006

Name: _____   **Date:** _____

Read the words in the word bank.

WORD BANK

brought	cough	enough
bought	through	tough
though	ought	thought

Write the words in alphabetical order.

_____   _____   _____

_____   _____   _____

_____   _____   _____

Now read these **ough** words with your teacher and write them on the lines.

rough   nought   trough

_____   _____   _____

Write a sentence containing at least one **ough** word.

_____

_____

_____

Name: _____   **Date:** _____

Words for today

though   _____

through   _____

bought   _____

brought   _____

thought   _____

cough   _____

tough   _____

enough   _____

ought   _____

10a

Learning objective

Phonemes
Consonants: /d/,/t/,/k/,/l/,/d/,/n/,/s/, /w/,/th/
Vowels: /or/,/a/ or /ar/ (according to region), /ee/,/e/,/i/,/ow/

Target words
daughter, taught, caught, laugh, laughed, naughtier, naughty, naughtiness, without

Worksheet 10a

- Photocopy this page and ask the child to cut out the target words.
- Discuss the words and what each word means. Help the child to read them by blending the phonemes.
- Ask him/her to identify the sounds in the word *taught* and the word *laugh*. Can the child hear the difference between the two sounds made by the grapheme **augh**? Pay particular attention to the words *naughty*, *naughtier* and *naughtiness*. Show the children how the letter **y** changes to a letter **i** when an ending is added. This is a standard rule for words that end with **y**, where the **y** follows a consonant.
- Discuss which word is the 'odd one out' from the list – *without* because it does not contain the grapheme **augh**.

Worksheet 10b

- Discuss the words at the top of the sheet before dictating the following sentences to the child:

  My daughter laughed at the naughtiness of the dog.
  The puppy was even naughtier than the older dog.
  The dog caught a biscuit in the way that he had been taught.

- S/he may need help in segmenting each word into its phonemes to make it easier to spell. Say each word repeatedly and slowly, encouraging the child to hear the separate sounds.
- As an extra activity ask the child to make up a sentence and to write it down. Encourage the child to write clearly, following the school's handwriting policy for letter formation, and to start each sentence with a capital letter and to end it with a full stop.

Worksheet 10c

- This sheet includes the nine target words.
- It can be copied so that the left hand side can be used for display purposes and the right hand side can be used to provide the child with extra practice in writing the words. You could write each word on the first of the two writing lines so that the child can copy your writing underneath in the correct style used by your school.

TARGET WORDS

daughter	taught	caught
laugh	laughed	naughtier
naughty	without	naughtiness

Name: **Date:**

Read these words because you will need them in your sentences.

puppy   older   biscuit

⭐ Listen to your teacher. Write the sentences.

_____

_____

_____

_____

_____

_____

_____

_____

_____

_____

⭐ Now write a sentence of your own using some of the target words.

_____

_____

_____

Name: Date:

Words for today

daughter _____

taught _____

caught _____

laugh _____

laughed _____

naughty _____

naughtier _____

naughtiness _____

without _____

Learning objective

11a	**Phonemes**	**Target words**

Phonemes
Consonants: /s/,/p/,/r/,/k/,/l/,/t/,/m/,/d/, /b/,/f/,/n/,/h/,/ng/
Vowels: /e/,/i/,/ae/,/u/,/or/,/er/,/o/

Target words
sprinkle, kettle, comfortable, table, middle, uncomfortable, horrible, terrible, important

Worksheet 11a

● Photocopy this page and ask the child to cut out the target words.

● Discuss the words and what each word means. Help the child to read them by blending the phonemes.

● Ask him/her to keep repeating some of the words such as *comfortable* to try to identify the sounds. In this word the phonemes are /k/, /u/, /m/, /f/, /t/, /er/, /b/, /u/, /l/. The sounds are not easy to distinguish but by repeating a word over and over again, while at the same time looking at the structure of the word, the child will gain valuable skills in segmenting other words for spelling.

● Discuss the fact that *important* is the 'odd one out' from the list as it does not contain the grapheme **le**.

Worksheet 11b

● Dictate the words **sprinkle, kettle, comfortable, table, middle, uncomfortable, horrible, terrible, important** to create the word bank at the top of the sheet.

● If the child is struggling with these difficult words, allow him/her to look again at the target words. S/he may need help in segmenting each word into its phonemes to make it easier to spell. Say each word repeatedly and slowly, encouraging the child to hear the separate sounds.

● Ensure that the child has spelt all the words correctly before asking him/her to fill in the sentences.

● As an extra activity ask the child to make up a sentence using the target words and to write it down. Encourage the child to write clearly, following the school's handwriting policy for letter formation, and to start each sentence with a capital letter and to end it with a full stop.

Worksheet 11c

● This sheet includes the nine target words.

● It can be copied so that the left hand side can be used for display purposes and the right hand side can be used to provide the child with extra practice in writing the words. You could write each word on the first of the two writing lines so that the child can copy your writing underneath in the correct style used by your school.

TARGET WORDS

sprinkle	kettle	comfortable
table	middle	uncomfortable
horrible	terrible	important

Name: _____ **Date:** _____

Listen to your teacher. Write the words in the word bank.

WORD BANK

_____ _____ _____

_____ _____ _____

_____ _____ _____

Use the correct words to fill in the gaps in these sentences.

Mum decided to _____
the flowers with some water.

Put the _____ in the _____
of the _____ table.

Do you think the chair is _____
or _____.

It is very _____ to do your homework.

Write your own sentence using the words from the word bank.

_____

_____

_____

Words for today

sprinkle _____

kettle _____

middle _____

table _____

comfortable _____

uncomfortable _____

horrible _____

terrible _____

important _____

Andrew Brodie: Supporting Phonics & Spelling © A & C Black Publishers Ltd. 2006

Learning objective

Phonemes
Consonants: /l/,/m/ (as grapheme mb), /k/,/r/,/th/,/p/,/ng/
Vowels: /a/,/oe/,/o/,/u/,/i/,/ie/,/er/

Target words
lamb, comb, bomb, crumb, limb, climb, thumb, plumber, coming

Worksheet 12a

- Photocopy this page and ask the child to cut out the target words.
- Discuss the words and what each word means. Help the child to read them by blending the phonemes.
- Can the child identify that all the words except for *coming*, which is the 'odd one out', have a silent **b**? The concept of 'silent letters' is often fascinating to children.
- Ask the child to identify the sounds in some of the words. Encourage him/her to say each word carefully – can he/she hear that the letter **o** in comb makes the /oe/ sound but that the letter **o** in bomb makes the /o/ sound?

Worksheet 12b

- Help the child to write the words in alphabetical order. This is quite challenging as four of the words begin with the letter **c** and the child will need to look at the fourth letters of the words *comb* and *coming*.
- Ask him/her to create oral sentences to include some of the words or related words, then to write down one of the sentences e.g. *Is the plumber coming to mend the shower? I tried to climb the tree but I couldn't. I held the comb with my finger and thumb.* S/he may need help in segmenting each word into its phonemes to make it easier to spell. Say each word repeatedly and slowly, encouraging the child to hear the separate sounds.
- Encourage the child to write clearly, following the school's handwriting policy for letter formation, and to start each sentence with a capital letter and to end it with a full stop.

Worksheet 12c

- This sheet includes the nine target words.
- It can be copied so that the left hand side can be used for display purposes and the right hand side can be used to provide the child with extra practice in writing the words. You could write each word on the first of the two writing lines so that the child can copy your writing in underneath in the correct style used by your school.

TARGET WORDS

lamb	comb	bomb
crumb	limb	climb
thumb	plumber	coming

Andrew Brodie: Supporting Phonics & Spelling © A & C Black Publishers Ltd. 2006

12b **Name:**   **Date:**

Read the words in the word bank.

bomb   lamb   climb   comb   thumb

coming   crumb   plumber   limb

★ Write the words in alphabetical order.

_____   _____   _____

_____   _____   _____

_____   _____   _____

★ Write your own sentences using words from the word bank.

_____

_____

_____

_____

_____

_____

_____

_____

Andrew Brodie: Supporting Phonics & Spelling © A & C Black Publishers Ltd. 2006

Name: _____ **Date:** _____

Words for today

lamb _____

comb _____

bomb _____

crumb _____

limb _____

climb _____

thumb _____

plumber _____

coming _____

Andrew Brodie: Supporting Phonics & Spelling © A & C Black Publishers Ltd. 2006

Learning objective

Phonemes	Target words
Consonants: /n/,/t/,/k/,/l/,/f/,/v/,/z/,/th/ **Vowels:** /o/,/ee/,/oe/,/ie/,/or/	knot, knee, knock, kneel, know, knife, knives, knight, thought

Worksheet 13a

- Photocopy this page and ask the child to cut out the target words, all featuring the silent **k** except for the 'odd one out' *thought*. Ask him/her to blend the phonemes in each of the words e.g. the /n/, /ie/, /v/ and /z/ in *knives*. Encourage the child to notice that the silent **k** is followed by **n** in each of the words.

- Discuss which word is the 'odd one out' from the list – *thought* also has some silent letters: **g** and **h**.

Worksheet 13b

- Discuss the words at the top of the sheet, paying particular attention to the words *section* and *drawer*, before dictating the following sentences to the child:

  Do you know the name of a knight?
  I knocked my knee when I was kneeling on the floor.
  Put the knife in the knives section of the drawer.

- S/he may need help in segmenting each word into its phonemes to make it easier to spell. Say each word repeatedly and slowly, encouraging the child to hear the separate sounds.

- It is worth discussing the sentences with the child to enable him/her to gain some comprehension skills e.g. S/he may know the name of a football manager or a pop star who has been knighted.

- As an extra activity ask the child to make up a sentence including some of the target words and to write it down. Encourage the child to write clearly, following the school's handwriting policy for letter formation, and to start each sentence with a capital letter and to end it with a full stop.

Worksheet 13c

- This sheet includes the nine target words.

- It can be copied so that the left hand side can be used for display purposes and the right hand side can be used to provide the child with extra practice in writing the words. You could write each word on the first of the two writing lines so that the child can copy your writing underneath in the correct style used by your school.

TARGET WORDS

knot	knee	knock
kneel	know	knife
knives	knight	thought

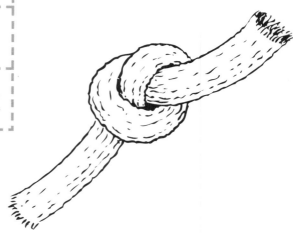

Name: **Date:**

Read these words because you will need them in your sentences.

name   floor   section   drawer

Listen to your teacher. Write the sentences.

Now write a sentence of your own using some of the target words.

Name: **Date:**

Words for today

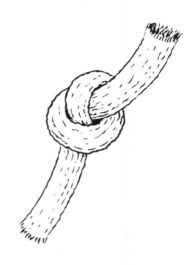

knot   _____

knee   _____

knock   _____

kneel   _____

know   _____

knife   _____

knives   _____

knight   _____

thought   _____

Learning objective

Phonemes	**Target words**
Consonants: /s/,/n/,/r/,/t/,/ng/,/p/, /g/,/l/,/h/,/b/,/w/ **Vowels:** /a/ or /ar/ (regional), /er/,/ie/,/i/, /oe/,/u/,/o/,/ue/,/ee/	answer, write, writing, wrote, wrap, wriggle, wrong, who, between

Worksheet 14a

- Photocopy this page and ask the child to cut out the target words.
- Discuss the words and what each word means. Help the child to read them by blending the phonemes.
- Ask him/her to identify the silent letter that appears in all of the words except the 'odd one out' word, *between*, where the letter **w** is not silent. Encourage the child to say each word repeatedly while looking closely at the letters.

Worksheet 14b

- Dictate the words **answer, sword, write, writing, wrote, wrap, wriggle, wrong, who, between** to create the word bank at the top of the sheet. If the child is struggling with these difficult words, allow him/her to look again at the target words. S/he may need help in segmenting each word into its phonemes to make it easier to spell. Say each word repeatedly and slowly, encouraging the child to hear the separate sounds.
- Ensure that the child has spelt all the words correctly before asking him/her to fill in the gaps in the sentences. The completed sentences are:

  Please write to Aunty Sue to answer the letter that she wrote to you.
  At night I like to wriggle down between the sheets.
  Do you know the difference between right and wrong?
  'Who is talking?' asked the teacher crossly.

- As an extra activity ask the child to make up a sentence using some of the target words and to write it down. Encourage the child to write clearly, following the school's handwriting policy for letter formation, and to start each sentence with a capital letter and to end it with a full stop.

Worksheet 14c

- This sheet includes the nine target words.
- It can be copied so that the left hand side can be used for display purposes and the right hand side can be used to provide the child with extra practice in writing the words. You could write each word on the first of the two writing lines so that the child can copy your writing underneath in the correct style used by your school.

TARGET WORDS

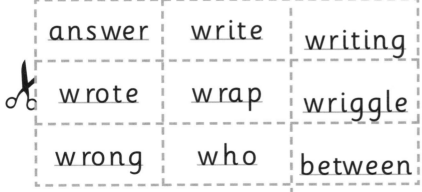

answer	write	writing
wrote	wrap	wriggle
wrong	who	between

Name: _____   **Date:** _____

Listen to your teacher. Write the words in the word bank.

WORD BANK

_____   _____   _____

_____   _____   _____

_____   _____   _____

★ Use the correct words to fill in the gaps in these sentences.

Please _____ to Aunty Sue to _____ the letter that she _____ to you.

At night I like to _____ down _____ the sheets.

Do you know the difference between right and _____?

"_____ is talking?" asked the teacher crossly.

★ Write your own sentence using some of the words from the word bank.

_____

_____

_____

Andrew Brodie: Supporting Phonics & Spelling © A & C Black Publishers Ltd. 2006

Name: _____ **Date:** _____

Words for today

answer _____

write _____

writing _____

wrote _____

wrap _____

wriggle _____

wrong _____

who _____

between _____

Learning objective

<table>
<tr><td>

15a

</td><td>

Phonemes
Consonants: /k/,/m/,/s/,/t/,/r/,/l/,/h/,/d/, /w/,/ng/
Vowels: /ie/,/e/,/i/,/ee/,/ue/,/or/,/a/,/ae/, /u/,/oe/

</td><td>

Target words
choir, school, chemistry, ache, stomach, orchestra, echo, swimming, headache

</td></tr>
</table>

Worksheet 15a

- Photocopy this page and ask the child to cut out the target words.

- Discuss the words and what each word means. Help the child to read them by blending the phonemes.

- Can the child identify what all the words have in common, except for *swimming*, which is the 'odd one out'? Point out that the word *headache* contains a spoken **h** as well as a silent **h**. The silent letter **h** in the grapheme **ch** is quite difficult to identify; notice that here the **ch** is saying k/ rather than /ch/. You may like to compare the word *choir* with the word *chair*, pointing out the different sounds made by the grapheme **ch**.

Worksheet 15b

- Help the child to write the words in alphabetical order.

- Ask him/her to create oral sentences to include some of the words or related words, then to write down one of the sentences e.g. *I had stomach ache so I couldn't go swimming. The school choir sang well with the school orchestra. The echo in the cave gave me a headache.* S/he may need help in segmenting each word into its phonemes to make it easier to spell. Say each word repeatedly and slowly, encouraging the child to hear the separate sounds.

- As an extra activity ask the child tomake up a sentence using some of the target words and to write it down. Encourage the child to write clearly, following the school's handwriting policy for letter formation, and to start each sentence with a capital letter and to end it with a full stop.

Worksheet 15c

- This sheet includes the nine target words.

- It can be copied so that the left hand side can be used for display purposes and the right hand side can be used to provide the child with extra practice in writing the words. You could write each word on the first of the two writing lines so that the child can copy your writing underneath in the correct style used by your school.

TARGET WORDS

choir	school	chemistry
ache	stomach	orchestra
echo	swimming	headache

Andrew Brodie: Supporting Phonics & Spelling © A & C Black Publishers Ltd. 2006

Name: **Date:**

Read the words in the word bank.

WORD BANK

ache   choir   headache   school   chemistry
stomach   orchestra   echo   swimming

Write the words in alphabetical order.

_____   _____   _____

_____   _____   _____

_____   _____   _____

Write your own sentence using some of the words from the word bank.

_____

_____

_____

Name: _____   **Date:** _____

Words for today

choir _____

chemistry _____

school _____

orchestra _____

ache _____

headache _____

stomach _____

echo _____

swimming _____

Andrew Brodie: Supporting Phonics & Spelling © A & C Black Publishers Ltd. 2006

16a

Learning objective

Phonemes

Consonants: /f/,/s/,/k/,/l/,/w/ or /wh/ (regional), /n/,/g/,/m/,/t/,/r/,/th/

Vowels: /a/ or /ar/ (regional), /er/,/oe/,/i/, /u/,/ue/,/e/

Target words

fasten, castle, mistletoe, whistle, listen, Christmas, soften, glisten, together

Worksheet 16a

- Photocopy this page and ask the child to cut out the target words, all featuring the silent **t** except for the 'odd one out' word, *together*. Ask him/her to blend the phonemes in each of the words. Encourage the child to notice that the silent **t** usually follows /s/ but that in *soften* it follows /f/.
- Discuss which word is the 'odd one out' from the list – the **t** in together is not silent and, of course, the letter **t** also appears in the phoneme /th/.

Worksheet 16b

- Discuss the words at the top of the sheet before dictating the following sentences to the child:

  As the knight left the castle he began to whistle.
  You often see mistletoe at Christmas.
  Fasten the two bits of string together.

- S/he may need help in segmenting each word into its phonemes to make it easier to spell. Say each word repeatedly and slowly, encouraging the child to hear the separate sounds.
- As an extra activity ask the child to make up a sentence using some of the target words and to write it down. Encourage the child to write clearly, following the school's handwriting policy for letter formation, and to start each sentence with a capital letter and to end it with a full stop.

Worksheet 16c

- This sheet includes the nine target words.
- It can be copied so that the left hand side can be used for display purposes and the right hand side can be used to provide the child with extra practice in writing the words. You could write each word on the first of the two writing lines so that the child can copy your writing in the correct style used by your school.

TARGET WORDS

fasten	castle	mistletoe
whistle	listen	Christmas
soften	glisten	together

Name: **Date:**

Read these words because you will need them in your sentences.

began   often   two   string

★ Listen to your teacher. Write the sentences.

_____

_____

_____

_____

_____

_____

_____

_____

★ Now write a sentence of your own using some of the target words.

_____

_____

_____

_____

_____

_____

Andrew Brodie: Supporting Phonics & Spelling © A & C Black Publishers Ltd. 2006

Name: **Date:**

Words for today

fasten _____

castle _____

mistletoe _____

whistle _____

listen _____

Christmas _____

soften _____

glisten _____

together _____

17a

Learning objective

Phonemes
Consonants: /s/,/n/,/d/,/k/,/f/,/v/,/z/,/h/, /t/,/m/
Vowels: /or/,/ie/,/i/,/ar/,/u/

Target words
gnaw, sign, design, calf, calves, half, halves, autumn, hymn

Worksheet 17a

- Photocopy this page and ask the child to cut out the target words.

- Discuss the words and what each word means. Help the child to read them by blending the phonemes. We have not included an 'odd one out' word in this list due to the complexity and variety of these silent letter words.

- Explain that there are three different silent letters in use in the target words: **g**, **l** and **n**. Help the child sort the words into sets according to the silent letters.

- Can the child identify similarities between words, e.g. *calf* and *half*, *calves* and *halves*?

Worksheet 17b

- Dictate the words to create the word bank at the top of the sheet.

- If the child is struggling with these difficult words, allow him/her to look again at the target words. S/he may need help in segmenting each word into its phonemes to make it easier to spell. Say each word repeatedly and slowly, encouraging the child to hear the separate sounds.

- Ensure that the child has spelt all the words correctly before asking him/her to write the words into the correct 'silent letter boxes'.

- As an extra activity ask the child to make up a sentence using some of the target words and to write it down. Encourage him/her to write clearly, following the school's handwriting policy for letter formation, and to start each sentence with a capital letter and to end it with a full stop

Worksheet 17c

- This sheet includes the nine target words.

- It can be copied so that the left hand side can be used for display purposes and the right hand side can be used to provide the child with extra practice in writing the words. You could write each word on the first of the two writing lines so that the child can copy your writing underneath in the correct style used by your school.

TARGET WORDS

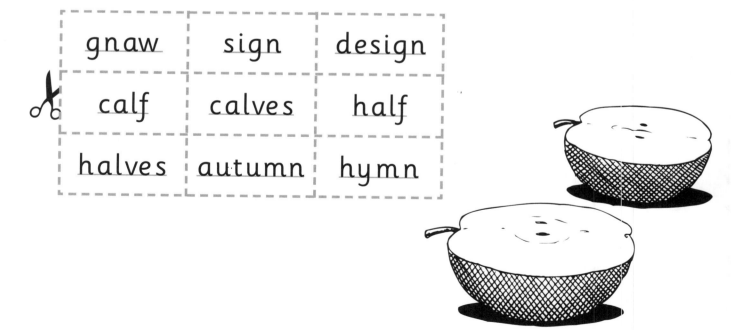

gnaw	sign	design
calf	calves	half
halves	autumn	hymn

Name: **Date:**

Listen to your teacher. Write the words in the word bank.

WORD BANK

_____   _____   _____

_____   _____   _____

_____   _____   _____

Write the words in the correct boxes.

silent g	**silent l**	**silent n**

Write your own sentence using words
from the word bank.

_____

_____

_____

Andrew Brodie: Supporting Phonics & Spelling © A & C Black Publishers Ltd. 2006

Name: **Date:**

Words for today

gnaw   _____

sign   _____

design   _____

calf   _____

calves   _____

half   _____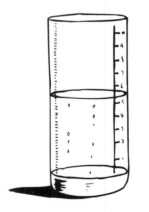

halves   _____

autumn   _____

hymn   _____

Learning objective

Phonemes
Consonants: /k/,/m/,/s/,/t/,/r/,/l/,/h/,/d/, /w/,/ng/
Vowels: /ie/,/e/,/i/,/ee/,/ue/,/or/,/a/,/ae/, /u/,/oe/

Target words
quiz, squash, quiet, quite, quarter, quality, quantity, antique, children

Worksheet 18a

- Photocopy this page and ask the child to cut out the target words.

- Discuss the words and what each word means. Help the child to read them by blending the phonemes.

- The 'odd one out' word on the list is *children*; all the other words include the grapheme **qu** which says the blend /k/ /w/ in most of the words but simply /k/ in *antique*.

- Encourage the child to break each of the longer words into syllables e.g. *quantity: quan-ti-ty*. To distinguish *quiet* from *quite* it is helpful to remember that *quiet* has two syllables *(qui-et)* whereas *quite* has only one. Remind the child of words such as *kite*, where the 'final **e**' is making the letter **i** say its name; the 'final **e**' is doing the same job in *quite*.

Worksheet 18b

- Help the child to write the words in alphabetical order. This list of words is particularly useful for this activity, as the child will need to look at the third or fourth letter of some of the words to decide the correct order.

- Ask the child to create oral sentences which include some of the words or related words and then to write down one of the sentences e.g. *The teacher told the children to be quite quiet. The lady bought a large quantity of good quality antiques. A quarter of the children had orange squash to drink*. Encourage the child to write clearly, following the school's handwriting policy for letter formation, and to start each sentence with a capital letter and to end it with a full stop.

Worksheet 18c

- This sheet includes the nine target words.

- It can be copied so that the left hand side can be used for display purposes and the right hand side can be used to provide the child with extra practice in writing the words. You could write each word on the first of the two writing lines so that the child can copy your writing underneath in the correct style used by your school.

TARGET WORDS

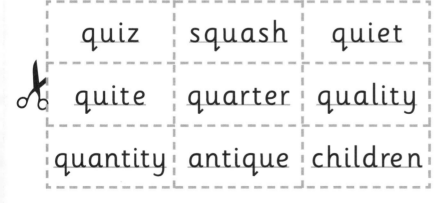

quiz	squash	quiet
quite	quarter	quality
quantity	antique	children

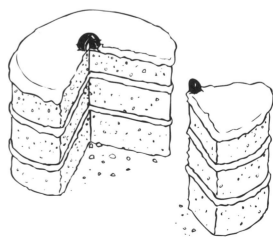

Name: **Date:**

Read the words in the word bank.

WORD BANK

squash	quarter	children	quiet	quantity

quality   quiz   antique   quite

★ Write the words in alphabetical order.

★ Write your own sentences using some of the words from the word bank.

Name: _____   **Date:** _____

Words for today

quiz   _____

squash   _____

quiet   _____

quite   _____

quarter _____

quality _____

quantity _____

antique _____

children _____

Learning objective

Phonemes **Consonants:** /k/,/l/,/f/,/v/,/r/,/t/,/h/,/b/, /n/,/j/,/y/ **Vowels:** /u/,/ae/,/ar/,/ur/,/ee/, /a/ or /ar/ (regional)	**Target words** colour, favourite, favour, flavour, hour, neighbour, journey, behaviour, asked

Worksheet 19a

- Photocopy this page and ask the child to cut out the target words. Ask him/her to blend the phonemes in each of the words.

- Encourage the child to notice that the grapheme **our** appears in all of the words except for the 'odd one out', *asked*. Many of the words on this list are used regularly by children, notably *colour*, *favourite*, *hour* and *asked*. Note that *hour* could be added to the list of silent **h** words.

Worksheet 19b

- Discuss the words at the top of the sheet before dictating the following sentences to the child:

  "Will you be on your best behaviour on the journey?" asked the teacher.
  "My neighbour's favourite colour is green but mine is red," said Raj.
  "I went to bed an hour late last night," said Jordan.

- S/he may need help in segmenting each word into its phonemes to make it easier to spell. Say each word repeatedly and slowly, encouraging the child to hear the separate sounds.

- Each of the three sentences features speech. You may like to show the child the sentences before dictating them, providing him/her with some clues for the spellings but also with some observations regarding the use of speech marks: e.g. The comma or question mark should be written before the closing speech marks.

- As an extra activity ask the child to make up a sentence using some of the target words and to write it down. Encourage him/her to write clearly, following the school's handwriting policy for letter formation, and to start each sentence with a capital letter and to end it with a full stop.

Worksheet 19c

- This sheet includes the nine target words.

- It can be copied so that the left hand side can be used for display purposes and the right hand side can be used to provide the child with extra practice in writing the words. You could write each word on the first of the two writing lines so that the child can copy your writing underneath in the correct style used by your school.

TARGET WORDS

colour	favour	favourite
flavour	hour	neighbour
journey	asked	behaviour

Name: **Date:**

Read these words because you will need them in your sentences.

teacher   green   mine   went   late

night   Raj   Jordan

Listen to your teacher. Write the sentences.

Now write your own sentence using some of the target words.

Words for today

colour

favourite

favour

flavour

hour

neighbour

journey

behaviour

asked